A GRAIN OF SAND

A GRAIN OF SAND

WILLIAM BLAKE

Poems for Young Readers
chosen and introduced by

ROSEMARY MANNING

with engravings by
WILLIAM BLAKE

international

FRANKLIN WATTS, INC.

575 Lexington Avenue
New York, N.Y. 10022

This selection and foreword © Rosemary Manning 1967
Library of Congress Catalog Card Number 68-18572
First American publication 1968 by Franklin Watts, Inc.
Printed in Great Britain by William Clowes & Sons Ltd, Beccles

ETERNITY

He who bends to himself a joy
Does the winged life destroy;
But he who kisses the joy as it flies
Lives in eternity's sun rise.

COMPILER'S NOTE

The poems and extracts printed in this selection have been taken from the Nonesuch Press edition of *The Complete Writings of William Blake*, edited by Geoffrey Keynes, published 1957.

Blake's own spelling and punctuation have been retained, for example 'tyger', 'recieved', 'siezed', 'ecchoing'. Blake used the syllable -ed for the past tense only when he intended the -ed to be sounded. If he did not require this, he wrote -'d, as in 'strip'd', 'leap'd', etc. Blake's use of capital letters, by which he emphasised certain words, has also been kept. He used 'and' and '&' indifferently, and this has been left exactly as printed in the Keynes edition.

For information about Blake and his work, the author of the introduction is indebted chiefly to the following works:

Mona Wilson, *The Life of William Blake* (Nonesuch Press, 1927)
Geoffrey Keynes, *Blake Studies* (Hart-Davis, 1949)
Harold Bloom, *Blake's Apocalypse* (Gollancz, 1963)
J. Bronowski, *William Blake: A Man without a Mask* (Secker & Warburg, 1944).

ROSEMARY MANNING

THE VOICE OF WILLIAM BLAKE

William Blake was born in London on November 28th, 1757. As a boy he walked in 'the fields from Islington to Marybone', a far greener London than to-day, but in this city of lanes and hedgerows lay huddled streets and grimy alleys. Here was the dark side of London: the black-faced boys of the chimney-sweepers, trudging behind their masters calling, 'Sweep, sweep'; horses beaten as they dragged their loads over greasy cobbles; caged birds singing in gloomy windows; bare-foot poverty begging in the streets. Few men noticed such commonplaces, or allowed their consciences to be pricked by them, but they made a deep impression on this London boy. They reappeared in his poems throughout his life, and fired the indignation which burns in such lines as this:

> Is that trembling cry a song?
> Can it be a song of joy?
> And so many children poor?
> It is a land of poverty!

Blake's father was a hosier, and William, the second of his three sons, was born in the home above the family business in Golden Square, in the Soho district of London. It must soon have been obvious to his parents that their middle son was a perplexing and extraordinary being. When William was only four, he declared that God looked in at the window upon him, and a few years later, he saw a tree in Peckham Rye surrounded by a host of angels. After Blake married, his younger brother, Robert, lived with the young couple, and died of consumption in their house. The

9

poet was deeply attached to him and recorded that he saw Robert's soul 'ascend heavenward . . . clapping its hands for joy'. Years later he was still aware of Robert's presence in the house, and wrote to a friend, William Hayley: 'Thirteen years ago I lost a brother, and with his spirit I converse daily and hourly in the spirit, and see him in my remembrance, in the regions of my imagination. I hear his advice, and even now write from his dictate'.

Fortunately, Blake's father must have realised that a boy with such visionary gifts, about which he spoke openly, would find it hard to fit into school life, and Blake was taught to read and write at home. Moreover, although the Blakes were poor, they had sufficient money to buy for their son not only books but engravings of well-known paintings. As a small child, William showed some ability with his pencil, so his father sent him, at the age of ten, to a drawing school, and later apprenticed him to a well-known engraver, James Basire. His apprenticeship over, he became a student at the Royal Academy, but he was not to stay there long. He was already a rebel, with strong, indeed violent views on the great masters upon whose work he was supposed to be modelling himself. Raphael and Michelangelo were his gods. Rubens, Rembrandt and Coreggio he detested. One has to remember that Blake would have seen comparatively few original paintings by any old master. His knowledge was for the most part gained through studying copies or engravings of their work.

At this time, the principal of the Royal Academy was Sir Joshua Reynolds. Blake could see no merit in the portraits of Reynolds and his school, and never lost an opportunity of criticising and deriding the fashionable painters. He referred to them in such terms as 'Sir Joshua and his Gang of Cunning Hired Knaves'. He refused to submit to academic influence. 'How I did secretly Rage!' he wrote later. 'I also spoke my Mind.' It is not surprising that this rebellious and outspoken student soon left the Academy. His work as an engraver, however, brought him friends among the designers and artists of the time, among them two, John Flaxman and Henry Fuseli, who were to be close to him for many years.

In 1782, at the age of twenty-four, Blake married Catherine Boucher, daughter of a Battersea market-gardener. This beautiful and sensitive woman had had little schooling, but her husband taught her to write and draw and colour. It was in many ways a happy marriage. Catherine believed in her husband's visions, helped him in printing and colouring the engravings, and despite the growing poverty of their later years provided him with an orderly and well-run home, with a secret guinea always held in reserve for emergencies.

At first the young couple made a fairly good living. A clergyman, the Reverend Henry Mathew, and his wife, became interested in Blake's work. They provided capital to set him up in a print shop. They invited him to their gatherings of artistic and literary people, and it was at their house in Charlotte Street that Blake read aloud and sometimes sang to tunes of his own the poems he had been writing since he was a boy. The Mathews were enthusiastic, and they and Flaxman defrayed the cost of printing the poems in a small volume called *Poetical Sketches*, for which the Reverend Mathew wrote an insufferably condescending Preface, describing the poems as 'the production of an untutored youth'. Blake found patronage of this kind stifling. He ceased to visit the Mathew household, though he continued to see his fellow artist and friend, John Flaxman.

The Soho print shop was a failure financially, but it was here that Blake had an opportunity to work at his craft of engraver, and to perfect a process of engraving

11

his own poetry which is an essential part of his art. Instead of printing the poems in the usual way and engraving plates for illustrations, he treated each page of the book as a complete design. The text and picture were etched in relief on a copper plate, and as each page was printed, Blake coloured the letters and drawings, his wife sometimes assisting him in the work. She then bound the volumes up and they sold for prices ranging from three shillings to ten guineas. It was in this form that Blake's best-known poems were printed, *Songs of Innocence* in 1789, and the same collection together with *Songs of Experience* in 1794. They were not published or sold in bookshops in the usual way, and reached only a small public. After this, he produced no more collections of lyrics, though he continued to write short verses, couplets, epigrams, and fragments of verse throughout the rest of his life. Some of these are printed in this selection and come from what is known as *Blake's Notebook*, a volume of writings and drawings which he kept by him for forty years, using every corner of it, writing in the margins and inserting pages when he had no more space.

In 1795, Blake and his wife moved from Soho to Hercules Buildings, in Lambeth on the south side of the Thames. The poet had high hopes of selling his illuminated books, of which he had completed several, besides *Songs of Innocence and of Experience*. He had virtually abandoned the lyric form for a new type of verse of which more will be said later. The sales of his books were, however, pitifully small, and he turned to illustrating the works of others. His most substantial commission was to provide the designs and engravings for a very popular book, Young's *Night Thoughts*. He asked a hundred guineas for his work, and it gives some idea of his difficulties when you learn that the publisher whittled this down to twenty guineas. The venture was a failure, and only four parts of the work were published. Among Blake's many book illustrations were two outstanding series, the water-colour drawings for *The Book of Job*, and the wood-engravings for Dr Thornton's translation of *Virgil's Pastorals*. Both were done when Blake was in his sixties and at the height of his creative power. The engravings for the *Virgil* have been used to decorate this selection.

Two patrons were of material help to Blake during the difficult years when, in addition to his own failure to earn much, England was at war with France, and food was scarce and prices high. The first patron was by far the more discerning. He was a civil servant, by name Thomas Butts. For years he regularly bought Blake's work, building up a fine private collection. He also employed Blake for a time to teach drawing to his young son, at £26 a year.

Despite his money difficulties, Blake's years at Lambeth were a period of enormous creativity. More and more of his working time was given to long, visionary poems, sometimes known as 'prophetic books'. These are almost a diary of his inner thoughts. There is no single or easy interpretation of them, for the symbolic characters who people them, like Urizen, Enitharmon, Albion and Los, carry more than one meaning. Whatever was occupying Blake's mind at the time, hatred of oppression, indignation against a one-time friend or patron, personal joy or unhappiness, visions of the new Jerusalem, all find their way into the prophetic books, that were no night visions or fantasies, but the stuff of Blake's everyday life. 'I am under the direction of Messengers from Heaven, Daily and Nightly', he wrote in a letter to his friend, Thomas Butts. The letter was written from Felpham, on the Sussex coast, where Blake had gone to live at the request of his other patron, William Hayley.

13

Hayley had known Blake for some time, for he was a member of the Mathews' literary circle where Blake had read his early poems. He was himself a poet, if a very inferior one, though he imagined that he was a considerable genius and a champion of good taste. He was well meaning, however, and genuinely wished to help Blake when he invited him to live at Felpham and assist him in some of his literary work. At that time, the year 1800, there was near-starvation among the poor in England, and the Blakes must have been thankful for Hayley's patronage. It was as well for them that they had no children to support and were content with a life of the utmost simplicity, provided it gave Blake freedom as a poet and artist.

At first, he was enthusiastic about Felpham, and described it as:

> A sweet place for Study, because it is more Spiritual than London. Heaven opens here on all sides her golden Gates . . . voices of Celestial inhabitants are more distinctly heard, & their forms more distinctly seen; & my Cottage is also a Shadow of their houses.

Alas, William Hayley proved a possessive patron, who expected Blake to act as his secretary and assist him with his own feeble and sentimental verses. Blake grew restive, and chafed against this bondage. The springs of his creativity began to dry up. As he put it: 'The Visions were angry with me at Felpham'. He returned to London and independence, even though it meant increasing poverty.

Although Blake was so at variance with the prevailing thought and artistic taste of his age, he was more of a private rebel than a public one. He was not an agitator or an orator. He did not suffer persecution or imprisonment like some of his free-thinking contemporaries, though on one occasion he came near to it. He was involved in an argument with a soldier while he was at

14

Felpham, and a charge of uttering treasonable words was brought against him. Hayley helped him through the trial, and he was found not guilty. It had been a frightening and humiliating experience, and though he went free, the trial must have served to emphasise his bitter sense of isolation from the materialistic, war-ridden world in which he lived. This sometimes finds its way into his verse, as in these intensely personal lines:

> O why was I born with a different face?
> Why was I not born like the rest of my race?

He would neither write nor paint to please patrons or fashion, nor would he keep silent about a world which contained so much injustice, hypocrisy and cruelty. His beliefs as a man and his visionary genius as an artist compelled him to follow paths which aroused mockery and suspicion among many. He held an exhibition of his paintings in 1809, but few came to see it, and it was cruelly attacked in Leigh Hunt's paper, the *Examiner*. In an article by Hunt's brother, Robert, Blake was described as 'an unfortunate lunatic whose personal inoffensiveness secures him from confinement'.

In his later years, Blake's genius was recognised by a small band of younger artists who called themselves the 'Ancients', and regarded Blake as their master. Among them was John Linnell, who actually persuaded the Royal Academy to grant its one-time rebellious student a sum of £25. Another was Samuel Palmer, a fine landscape painter. Palmer left a vivid account of Blake as he appeared to his friends:

> Blake, once known, could never be forgotten. In him you saw at once the Maker, the Inventor; one of the few in any age; a fitting companion for Dante. He was energy itself, and shed around him a kindling influence, an atmosphere of life, full of the ideal. To walk with

15

him in the country was to perceive the soul of beauty through the forms of matter; and the high, gloomy buildings between which, from his study window, a glimpse was caught of the Thames and the Surrey shore, assumed a kind of grandeur from the man dwelling near them. Those may laugh at this who never knew such a one as Blake; but of him it is the simple truth.

He was a man without a mask; his aim single, his path straightforwards, and his wants few; so he was free, noble and happy. His voice and manner were quiet, yet all awake with intellect . . . He was gentle and affectionate, loving to be with little children and to talk about them. 'That is Heaven,' he said to a friend, leading him to a window, and pointing to a group of them at play.

Declining, like Socrates, whom in many respects he resembled, the common objects of ambition, and pitying the scuffle to obtain them, he thought that no one could be truly great who had not humbled himself 'even as a little child'. This was a subject which he loved to dwell upon and to illustrate . . . Such was Blake as I remember him.

*　　*　　*

The poems in this selection have been grouped together under different headings to help the reader to become familiar with the themes which occupied this extraordinary writer, who saw himself not only as a poet but as a seer or prophet, like Ezekiel or Isaiah, men who were not content merely to denounce the wickedness of men's ways but endeavoured to interpret their errors and lead them towards

Heaven's gate
Built in Jerusalem's wall.

Most of the lyrics are taken from *Songs of Innocence and of Experience*. Blake realised, very early in his life, that creation contains both good and evil, and to under-

16

stand the poems it is important to know the full title which he gave to his volume:

Songs of Innocence and of Experience Shewing the Two Contrary States of the Human Soul.

Several of the *Songs of Innocence* are echoed with a very different emphasis in *Songs of Experience*, which show the dark side of the human spirit. There are in this selection several pairs of poems expressing these 'contraries': the two entitled *Holy Thursday*, for instance, and the two versions of *The Chimney Sweeper*. One of his best-known poems, *The Tyger*, sums up the problem of these 'contraries'. It carries us past the image of the wild beast in its splendour and 'fearful symmetry' and confronts us with a profound question, and one which has troubled men since the conception of a divine creator first dawned in their minds:

Did he who made the Lamb make thee?

The Tyger is not simply an animal poem, but contains the kernel of a theme which Blake continued to develop and work upon in his later poetry. He brought to bear on the problem of good and evil an imagination so powerful and intense that it reaches to a reality beyond that of the visible world. He believed that his own intensity of vision was within the grasp of every mind, but that men were blind to revelations offered them on every side. 'If the doors of perception were cleansed,' he wrote, 'everything would appear to man as it is, infinite.' He expresses this in another form in the words which head a long poem called *Auguries of Innocence*, from which the title of this book is taken:

To see a World in a Grain of Sand
And a Heaven in a Wild Flower,
Hold Infinity in the palm of your hand
And Eternity in an hour.

The 'auguries' or signs of innocence are close at hand and it is for us to grasp them, understand them, and renew our lives in their light. Only a belief that 'everything that lives is holy' can bring us in touch with the infinite and release in us the power of love, mercy and pity, which will subdue the 'contrary states' of hatred and cruelty.

It would have been unjust to Blake to omit from this selection any excerpts from the 'prophetic books' which contain so much of the essential man and poet. It is impossible to summarise their contents, but the following short account of some of them may be helpful to anyone reading the last section of this book, *Jerusalem's Pillars*.

Among the early long poems, *The Everlasting Gospel* contains a theme that was to reappear again and again in Blake's work: that conventional Christianity was not a true expression of the message of Christ, and indeed was often a perversion of it, for the churches in Blake's time were over-willing to appear on the side of the wealthy and secure, and did little to champion the cause of the poor and oppressed. Blake's youth had been lived through a time of revolution abroad, in America and France, and of deep poverty and violent change in England, where the rapid growth of manufacturing towns was taking men away from the countryside to work in mines and factories in conditions of squalor, for the increasing profit of the owners of the new industries. Blake denounced the materialistic doctrines popular in this day, doctrines which proclaimed the virtues of being rich and respectable, and regarded the labouring classes as almost a separate species, placed in a lowly social position by a wise providence; as Mrs Alexander, the Victorian hymn-writer expressed it in 'All things bright and beautiful':

18

The rich man in his castle,
The poor man at his gate,
God made them, high or lowly,
And order'd their estate.

Two of the early prophetic books, *America* and *The French Revolution*, attacked political and social injustice, but Blake was rapidly moving towards a far larger theme. This becomes clear in the long poem, *Vala or The Four Zoas*, of which several extracts are given in the last section of this book. It reached its finest expression in *Milton* and *Jerusalem*, the epics which brought to a close Blake's poetic work. The theme is the building of a new Jerusalem through the release of man's creative energy, a city which will enfold and transform the old world of material greed and imprisoned imagination. Such a simple statement as this is intended as no more than a mere starting-point. One can only ask the reader to follow Blake himself through the lyrics to the prophetic books, with a heart and mind open to whatever meaning they may spell out for him. Writing about one of his own paintings, Blake said: 'If the Spectator could Enter into these Images in his Imagination, approaching them on the Fiery Chariot of his Contemplative Thought . . . then would he arise from his Grave'. It is in this spirit that the reader will find most reward in the poetry of Blake.

Blake is a poet who 'opens the doors of perception'. The man who as a boy heard 'the music of an angel's tongue' wrote in the last of the prophetic books, *Jerusalem*:

I rest not from my great task!
To open the Eternal Worlds, to open the immortal Eyes
Of Man inwards into the Worlds of Thought, into
    Eternity.

19

Jerusalem was written when Blake and his wife were living in great poverty in London, towards the end of his life. He died on August 12th, 1827, aged seventy, 'a man without a mask', whose face few men of his own time recognised. One of the younger members of the 'Ancients', the painter George Richmond, wrote to Samuel Palmer:

My dr. friend
Lest you should not have heard of the Death of Mr. Blake I have written this to inform you——He died on Sunday Night at 6 o'clock in a most glorious manner. He said He was going to that Country he had all his life wished to see & expressed himself Happy hoping for Salvation through Jesus Christ——Just before he died His countenance became fair——His eyes Brighten'd and He burst out in singing of the things he saw in Heaven.

ROSEMARY MANNING

CONTENTS

Two Contrary States

The Peaceable Kingdom

Jerusalem's Pillars

The Echoing Green

INTRODUCTION

TO SONGS OF INNOCENCE

Piping down the valleys wild,
Piping songs of pleasant glee,
On a cloud I saw a child,
And he laughing said to me:

"Pipe a song about a Lamb!"
So I piped with merry chear.
"Piper, pipe that song again;"
So I piped: he wept to hear.

"Drop thy pipe, thy happy pipe;
"Sing thy songs of happy chear:"
So I sung the same again,
While he wept with joy to hear.

"Piper, sit thee down and write
"In a book that all may read."
So he vanish'd from my sight,
And I pluck'd a hollow reed,

And I made a rural pen,
And I stain'd the water clear,
And I wrote my happy songs
Every child may joy to hear.

A DREAM

Once a dream did weave a shade
O'er my Angel-guarded bed,
That an Emmet lost its way
Where on grass methought I lay.

Troubled, 'wilder'd, and forlorn,
Dark, benighted, travel-worn,
Over many a tangled spray,
All heart-broke I heard her say:

"O, my children! do they cry?
"Do they hear their father sigh?
"Now they look abroad to see:
"Now return and weep for me."

Pitying, I drop'd a tear;
But I saw a glow-worm near,
Who replied: "What wailing wight
"Calls the watchman of the night?

"I am set to light the ground,
"While the beetle goes his round:
"Follow now the beetle's hum;
"Little wanderer, hie thee home."

THE SHEPHERD

How sweet is the Shepherd's sweet lot!
From the morn to the evening he strays;
He shall follow his sheep all the day,
And his tongue shall be filled with praise.

For he hears the lamb's innocent call,
And he hears the ewe's tender reply;
He is watchful while they are in peace,
For they know when their Shepherd is nigh.

TO MORNING

O holy virgin! clad in purest white,
Unlock heav'n's golden gates, and issue forth;
Awake the dawn that sleeps in heaven; let light
Rise from the chambers of the east, and bring
The honied dew that cometh on waking day.
O radiant morning, salute the sun,
Rouz'd like a huntsman to the chace, and, with
Thy buskin'd feet, appear upon our hills.

TO WINTER

O Winter! bar thine adamantine doors:
The north is thine; there hast thou built thy dark
Deep-founded habitation. Shake not they roofs,
Nor bend they pillars with thine iron car.

He hears me not, but o'er the yawning deep
Rides heavy; his storms are unchain'd, sheathed
In ribbed steel; I dare not lift mine eyes,
For he hath rear'd his sceptre o'er the world.

Lo! now the dircful monster, whose skin clings
To his strong bones, strides o'er the groaning rocks:
He withers all in silence, and his hand
Unclothes the earth, and freezes up frail life.

He takes his seat upon the cliffs; the mariner
Cries in vain. Poor little wretch! that deal'st
With storms, till heaven smiles, and the monster
Is driv'n yelling to his caves beneath mount Hecla.

THE ECCHOING GREEN

The Sun does arise,
And make happy the skies;
The merry bells ring
To welcome the Spring;
The skylark and thrush,
The birds of the bush,
Sing louder around
To the bells' chearful sound,
While our sports shall be seen
On the Ecchoing Green.

Old John, with white hair,
Does laugh away care,
Sitting under the oak,
Among the old folk.
They laugh at our play,
And soon they all say:
"Such, such were the joys
"When we all, girls & boys,
"In our youth time were seen
"On the Ecchoing Green."

Till the little ones, weary,
No more can be merry;
The sun does descend,
And our sports have an end.
Round the laps of their mothers
Many sisters and brothers,
Like birds in their nest,
Are ready for rest,
And sport no more seen
On the darkening Green.

31

Into the Dangerous
World

A CRADLE SONG

Sleep, Sleep, beauty bright
Dreaming o'er the joys of night
Sleep, Sleep: in thy sleep
Little sorrows sit & weep.

Sweet Babe, in thy face
Soft desires I can trace
Secret joys & secret smiles
Little pretty infant wiles.

As thy softest limbs I feel
Smiles as of the morning steal
O'er thy cheek & o'er thy breast
Where thy little heart does rest.

O, the cunning wiles that creep
In thy little heart asleep.
When thy little heart does wake,
Then the dreadful lightnings break.

From thy cheek & from thy eye
O'er the youthful harvests nigh
Infant wiles & infant smiles
Heaven & Earth of peace beguiles.

INFANT SORROW

AN EXTRACT

My mother groan'd, my father wept;
Into the dangerous world I leapt,
Helpless, naked, piping loud,
Like a fiend hid in a cloud.

Struggling in my father's hands
Striving against my swaddling bands,
Bound & weary, I thought best
To sulk upon my mother's breast.

When I saw that rage was vain,
And to sulk would nothing gain,
Turning many a trick & wile,
I began to soothe & smile.

And I sooth'd day after day
Till upon the ground I stray;
And I smil'd night after night,
Seeking only for delight.

And I saw before me shine
Clusters of the wand'ring vine
And many a lovely flower & tree
Stretch'd their blossoms out to me.

My father then with holy look,
In his hands a holy book,
Pronounc'd curses on my head
And bound me in a mirtle shade . . .

IN A MIRTLE SHADE

Why should I be bound to thee,
O my lovely mirtle tree?
Love, free love, cannot be bound
To any tree that grows on ground.

O, how sick & weary I
Underneath my mirtle lie,
Like to dung upon the ground
Underneath my mirtle bound.

Oft my mirtle sigh'd in vain
To behold my heavy chain
Oft my father saw us sigh,
And laugh'd at our simplicity.

So I smote him & his gore
Stain'd the roots my mirtle bore.
But the time of youth is fled,
And grey hairs are on my head.

THE SCHOOL BOY

I love to rise in a summer morn
When the birds sing on every tree;
The distant huntsman winds his horn,
And the sky-lark sings with me.
O! what sweet company.

But to go to school in a summer morn,
O! it drives all joy away;
Under a cruel eye outworn,
The little ones spend the day
In sighing and dismay.

Ah! then at times I drooping sit,
And spend many an anxious hour,
Nor in my book can I take delight,
Nor sit in learning's bower,
Worn thro' with the dreary shower.

How can the bird that is born for joy
Sit in a cage and sing?
How can a child, when fears annoy,
But droop his tender wing,
And forget his youthful spring?

O! father & mother, if buds are nip'd
And blossoms blown away,
And if the tender plants are strip'd
Of their joy in the springing day,
By sorrow and care's dismay,

How shall the summer arise in joy,
Or the summer fruits appear?
Or how shall we gather what griefs destroy,
Or bless the mellowing year,
When the blasts of winter appear?

THE CRYSTAL CABINET

The Maiden caught me in the Wild,
Where I was dancing merrily;
She put me into her Cabinet
And Lock'd me up with a golden Key.

This Cabinet is form'd of Gold
And Pearl & Crystal shining bright,
And within it opens into a World
And a little lovely Moony Night.

Another England there I saw,
Another London with its Tower,
Another Thames & other Hills,
And another pleasant Surrey Bower,

Another Maiden like herself,
Translucent, lovely, shining clear,
Threefold each in the other clos'd—
O, what a pleasant trembling fear!

O, what a smile! a threefold Smile
Fill'd me, that like a flame I burn'd;
I bent to Kiss the lovely Maid,
And found a Threefold Kiss return'd.

I strove to sieze the inmost Form
With ardor fierce & hands of flame,
But burst the Crystal Cabinet,
And like a Weeping Babe became—

A weeping Babe upon the wild,
And Weeping Woman pale reclin'd,
And in the outward air again
I fill'd with woes the passing Wind.

The Silken Net

SONG

How sweet I roam'd from field to field,
    And tasted all the summer's pride,
'Till I the prince of love beheld,
    Who in the sunny beams did glide!

He shew'd me lilies for my hair,
    And blushing roses for my brow;
He led me through his gardens fair,
    Where all his golden pleasures grow.

With sweet May dews my wings were wet,
    And Phœbus fir'd my vocal rage;
He caught me in his silken net,
    And shut me in his golden cage.

He loves to sit and hear me sing,
    Then, laughing, sports and plays with me;
Then stretches out my golden wing,
    And mocks my loss of liberty.

SONG

Love and harmony combine,
And around our souls intwine,
While thy branches mix with mine,
And our roots together join.

Joys upon our branches sit,
Chirping loud, and singing sweet;
Like gentle streams beneath our feet
Innocence and virtue meet.

Thou the golden fruit dost bear,
I am clad in flowers fair;
Thy sweet boughs perfume the air,
And the turtle buildeth there.

There she sits and feeds her young,
Sweet I hear her mournful song;
And thy lovely leaves among,
There is love: I hear his tongue.

There his charming nest doth lay,
There he sleeps the night away;
There he sports along the day,
And doth among our branches play.

THE GARDEN OF LOVE

I went to the Garden of Love,
And saw what I never had seen:
A Chapel was built in the midst,
Where I used to play on the green.

And the gates of this Chapel were shut,
And "Thou shalt not" writ over the door;
So I turn'd to the Garden of Love
That so many sweet flowers bore;

And I saw it was filled with graves,
And tomb-stones where flowers should be;
And Priests in black gowns were walking their
    rounds,
And binding with briars my joys & desires.

I FEAR'D THE FURY

I fear'd the fury of my wind
Would blight all blossoms fair & true;
And my sun it shin'd & shin'd
And my wind it never blew.

But a blossom fair or true
Was not found on any tree;
For all blossoms grew & grew
Fruitless, false, tho' fair to see.

NEVER PAIN
TO TELL THY LOVE

Never pain to tell thy love
Love that never told can be;
For the gentle wind does move
Silently, invisibly.

I told my love, I told my love,
I told her all my heart,
Trembling, cold, in ghastly fears—
Ah, she doth depart.

Soon as she was gone from me
A traveller came by
Silently, invisibly—
O, was no deny.

THE SICK ROSE

O Rose, thou art sick!
The invisible worm
That flies in the night,
In the howling storm,

Has found out thy bed
Of crimson joy:
And his dark secret love
Does thy life destroy.

AH! SUN-FLOWER

Ah, Sun-flower, weary of time,
Who countest the steps of the Sun,
Seeking after that sweet golden clime
Where the traveller's journey is done:

Where the Youth pined away with desire,
And the pale Virgin shrouded in snow
Arise from their graves, and aspire
Where my Sun-flower wishes to go.

A POISON TREE

I was angry with my friend:
I told my wrath, my wrath did end.
I was angry with my foe:
I told it not, my wrath did grow.

And I water'd it in fears,
Night & morning with my tears;
And I sunned it with smiles,
And with soft deceitful wiles.

And it grew both day and night,
Till it bore an apple bright;
And my foe beheld it shine,
And he knew that it was mine,

And into my garden stole
When the night had veil'd the pole:
In the morning glad I see
My foe outstretch'd beneath the tree.

Two Contrary States

AUGURIES OF INNOCENCE

AN EXTRACT

To see a World in a Grain of Sand
And a Heaven in a Wild Flower,
Hold Infinity in the palm of your hand
And Eternity in an hour.

A Robin Red breast in a Cage
Puts all Heaven in a Rage.
A dove house fill'd with doves & Pigeons
Shudders Hell thro' all its regions.
A dog starv'd at his Master's Gate
Predicts the ruin of the State.
A Horse misus'd upon the Road
Calls to Heaven for Human blood.
Each outcry of the hunted Hare
A fibre from the Brain does tear.
A Skylark wounded in the wing,
A Cherubim does cease to sing.
The Game Cock clip'd & arm'd for fight
Does the Rising Sun affright . . .

LONDON

I wander thro' each charter'd street,
Near where the charter'd Thames does flow,
And mark in every face I meet
Marks of weakness, marks of woe.

In every cry of every Man,
In every Infant's cry of fear,
In every voice, in every ban,
The mind-forg'd manacles I hear.

How the Chimney-sweeper's cry
Every black'ning Church appalls;
And the hapless Soldier's sigh
Runs in blood down Palace walls.

But most thro' midnight streets I hear
How the youthful Harlot's curse
Blasts the new born Infant's tear,
And blights with plagues the Marriage hearse.

HOLY THURSDAY

Is this a holy thing to see
In a rich and fruitful land,
Babes reduc'd to misery,
Fed with cold and usurous hand?

Is that trembling cry a song?
Can it be a song of joy?
And so many children poor?
It is a land of poverty!

And their sun does never shine,
And their fields are bleak & bare,
And their ways are fill'd with thorns:
It is eternal winter there.

For where-e'er the sun does shine,
And where-e'er the rain does fall,
Babe can never hunger there,
Nor poverty the mind appall.

HOLY THURSDAY

'Twas on a Holy Thursday, their innocent faces clean,
The children walking two & two, in red & blue &
    green,
Grey-headed beadles walk'd before, with wands as
    white as snow,
Till into the high dome of Paul's they like Thames'
    waters flow.

O what a multitude they seem'd, these flowers of
    London town!
Seated in companies they sit with radiance all their
    own.
The hum of multitudes was there, but multitudes of
    lambs,
Thousands of little boys & girls raising their innocent
    hands.

Now like a mighty wind they raise to heaven the voice
    of song,
Or like harmonious thunderings the seats of Heavens
    among.
Beneath them sit the aged men, wise guardians of the
    poor;
Then cherish pity, lest you drive an angel from your
    door.

THE CHIMNEY SWEEPER

When my mother died I was very young,
And my Father sold me while yet my tongue
Could scarcely cry "'weep! 'weep! 'weep! 'weep!"
So your chimneys I sweep, & in soot I sleep.

There's little Tom Dacre, who cried when his head,
That curl'd like a lamb's back, was shav'd: so I said
"Hush, Tom! never mind it, for when your head's
    bare
"You know that the soot cannot spoil your white hair."

And so he was quiet, & that very night
As Tom was a-sleeping, he had such a sight!
That thousands of sweepers, Dick, Joe, Ned, & Jack,
Were all of them lock'd up in coffins of black.

And by came an Angel who had a bright key,
And he open'd the coffins & set them all free;
Then down a green plain leaping, laughing, they run,
And wash in a river, and shine in the Sun.

Then naked & white, all their bags left behind,
They rise upon clouds and sport in the wind;
And the Angel told Tom, if he'd be a good boy,
He'd have God for his father, & never want joy.

And so Tom awoke; and we rose in the dark,
And got with our bags & our brushes to work.
Tho' the morning was cold, Tom was happy & warm;
So if all do their duty they need not fear harm.

THE CHIMNEY SWEEPER

A little black thing among the snow,
Crying "'weep! 'weep!" in notes of woe!
"Where are thy father & mother? say?"
"They are both gone up to the church to pray.

"Because I was happy upon the heath,
"And smil'd among the winter's snow,
"They clothed me in the clothes of death,
"And taught me to sing the notes of woe.

"And because I am happy & dance & sing,
"They think they have done me no injury,
"And are gone to praise God & his Priest &
    King,
"Who make up a heaven of our misery."

I HEARD AN ANGEL SINGING

I heard an Angel singing
When the day was springing,
"Mercy, Pity, Peace
"Is the world's release."

Thus he sung all day
Over the new mown hay,
Till the sun went down
And haycocks looked brown.

I heard a Devil curse
Over the heath & the furze,
"Mercy could be no more,
"If there was nobody poor,

"And pity no more could be,
"If all were as happy as we."
At his curse the sun went down,
And the heavens gave a frown.

And Miseries' increase
Is Mercy, Pity, Peace.

THE DIVINE IMAGE

To Mercy, Pity, Peace, and Love
All pray in their distress;
And to these virtues of delight
Return their thankfulness.

For Mercy, Pity, Peace, and Love
Is God, our father dear,
And Mercy, Pity, Peace, and Love
Is Man, his child and care.

For Mercy has a human heart,
Pity a human face,
And Love, the human form divine,
And Peace, the human dress.

Then every man, of every clime,
That prays in his distress,
Prays to the human form divine,
Love, Mercy, Pity, Peace.

And all must love the human form,
In heathen, turk, or jew;
Where Mercy, Love, & Pity dwell
There God is dwelling too.

A DIVINE IMAGE

Cruelty has a Human Heart,
And Jealousy a Human Face;
Terror the Human Form Divine,
And Secrecy the Human Dress.

The Human Dress is forged Iron,
The Human Form a fiery Forge,
The Human Face a Furnace seal'd,
The Human Heart its hungry Gorge.

THE TYGER

Tyger! Tyger! burning bright
In the forests of the night,
What immortal hand or eye
Could frame thy fearful symmetry?

In what distant deeps or skies
Burnt the fire of thine eyes?
On what wings dare he aspire?
What the hand dare sieze the fire?

And what shoulder, & what art,
Could twist the sinews of thy heart?
And when thy heart began to beat,
What dread hand? & what dread feet?

What the hammer? what the chain?
In what furnace was thy brain?
What the anvil? what dread grasp
Dare its deadly terrors clasp?

When the stars threw down their spears,
And water'd heaven with their tears,
Did he smile his work to see?
Did he who made the Lamb make thee?

Tyger! Tyger! burning bright
In the forests of the night,
What immortal hand or eye
Dare frame thy fearful symmetry?

The Peaceable Kingdom

THE LAMB

Little Lamb, who made thee?
Dost thou know who made thee?
Gave thee life, & bid thee feed
By the stream & o'er the mead;
Gave thee clothing of delight,
Softest clothing, wooly, bright;
Gave thee such a tender voice,
Making all the vales rejoice?
   Little Lamb, who made thee?
   Dost thou know who made thee?

   Little Lamb, I'll tell thee,
   Little Lamb, I'll tell thee:
He is called by thy name,
For he calls himself a Lamb.
He is meek, & he is mild;

He became a little child.
I a child, & thou a lamb,
We are called by his name.
   Little Lamb, God bless thee!
   Little Lamb, God bless thee!

THE LITTLE BLACK BOY

My mother bore me in the southern wild,
And I am black, but O! my soul is white;
White as an angel is the English child,
But I am black, as if bereav'd of light.

My mother taught me underneath a tree,
And sitting down before the heat of day,
She took me on her lap and kissed me,
And pointing to the east, began to say:

"Look on the rising sun: there God does live,
"And gives his light, and gives his heat away;
"And flowers and trees and beasts and men
        recieve
"Comfort in morning, joy in the noonday.

"And we are put on earth a little space,
"That we may learn to bear the beams of love;
"And these black bodies and this sunburnt face
"Is but a cloud, and like a shady grove.

"For when our souls have learn'd the heat to bear,
"The cloud will vanish; we shall hear his voice,
"Saying: 'Come out from the grove, my love &
        care,
" ' And round my golden tent like lambs rejoice.' "

Thus did my mother say, and kissed me;
And thus I say to little English boy.
When I from black and he from white cloud free,
And round the tent of God like lambs we joy,

I'll shade him from the heat, till he can bear
To lean in joy upon our father's knee;
And then I'll stand and stroke his silver hair,
And be like him, and he will then love me.

THE LITTLE GIRL LOST

In futurity
I prophetic see
That the earth from sleep
(Grave the sentence deep)

Shall arise and seek
For her maker meek;
And the desart wild
Become a garden mild.

In the southern clime,
Where the summer's prime
Never fades away,
Lovely Lyca lay.

Seven summers old
Lovely Lyca told;
She had wander'd long
Hearing wild birds' song.

"Sweet sleep, come to me
"Underneath this tree.
"Do father, mother weep,
"Where can Lyca sleep?

"Lost in desart wild
"Is your little child.
"How can Lyca sleep
"If her mother weep?

"If her heart does ake
"Then let Lyca wake;
"If my mother sleep,
"Lyca shall not weep.

"Frowning, frowning night,
"O'er this desart bright
"Let thy moon arise
"While I close my eyes."

Sleeping Lyca lay
While the beasts of pray,
Come from caverns deep,
View'd the maid asleep.

The kingly lion stood
And the virgin view'd,
Then he gambol'd round
O'er the hallow'd ground.

Leopards, tygers, play
Round her as she lay,
While the lion old
Bow'd his mane of gold

And her bosom lick,
And upon her neck
From his eyes of flame
Ruby tears there came;

While the lioness
Loos'd her slender dress,
And naked they convey'd
To caves the sleeping maid.

THE LITTLE GIRL FOUND

All the night in woe
Lyca's parents go
Over vallies deep,
While the desarts weep.

Tired and woe-begone,
Hoarse with making moan,
Arm in arm seven days
They trac'd the desert ways.

Seven nights they sleep
Among shadows deep,
And dream they see their child
Starv'd in desert wild.

Pale, thro' pathless ways
The fancied image strays
Famish'd, weeping, weak,
With hollow piteous shriek.

Rising from unrest,
The trembling woman prest
With feet of weary woe:
She could no further go.

In his arms he bore
Her, arm'd with sorrow sore;
Till before their way
A couching lion lay.

Turning back was vain:
Soon his heavy mane
Bore them to the ground.
Then he stalk'd around,

Smelling to his prey;
But their fears allay
When he licks their hands,
And silent by them stands.

They look upon his eyes
Fill'd with deep surprise,
And wondering behold
A Spirit arm'd in gold.

On his head a crown,
On his shoulders down
Flow'd his golden hair.
Gone was all their care.

"Follow me," he said;
"Weep not for the maid;
"In my palace deep
"Lyca lies asleep."

Then they followed
Where the vision led,
And saw their sleeping child
Among tygers wild.

To this day they dwell
In a lonely dell;
Nor fear the wolvish howl
Nor the lions' growl.

ON ANOTHER'S SORROW

Can I see another's woe,
And not be in sorrow too?
Can I see another's grief,
And not seek for kind relief?

Can I see a falling tear,
And not feel my sorrow's share?
Can a father see his child
Weep, nor be with sorrow fill'd?

Can a mother sit and hear
An infant groan, an infant fear?
No, no! never can it be!
Never, never can it be!

And can he who smiles on all
Hear the wren with sorrows small,
Hear the small bird's grief & care,
Hear the woes that infants bear,

And not sit beside the nest,
Pouring pity in their breast;
And not sit the cradle near,
Weeping tear on infant's tear;

And not sit both night & day,
Wiping all our tears away?
O! no never can it be!
Never, never can it be!

He doth give his joy to all;
He becomes an infant small;
He becomes a man of woe;
He doth feel the sorrow too.

Think not thou canst sigh a sigh
And thy maker is not by;
Think not thou canst weep a tear
And thy maker is not near.

O! he gives to us his joy
That our grief he may destroy;
Till our grief is fled & gone
He doth sit by us and moan.

MORNING

To find the Western path
Right thro' the Gates of Wrath
I urge my way;
Sweet Mercy leads me on:
With soft repentant moan
I see the break of day.

The war of swords & spears
Melted by dewy tears
Exhales on high;
The Sun is freed from fears
And with soft grateful tears
Ascends the sky.

NIGHT

The sun descending in the west,
The evening star does shine;
The birds are silent in their nest,
And I must seek for mine.
The moon like a flower
In heaven's high bower,
With silent delight
Sits and smiles on the night.

Farewell, green fields and happy groves,
Where flocks have took delight.
Where lambs have nibbled, silent moves
The feet of angels bright;
Unseen they pour blessing
And joy without ceasing,
On each bud and blossom,
And each sleeping bosom.

They look in every thoughtless nest,
Where birds are cover'd warm;
They visit caves of every beast.
To keep them all from harm.
If they see any weeping
That should have been sleeping,
They pour sleep on their head,
And sit down by their bed.

When wolves and tygers howl for prey,
They pitying stand and weep;
Seeking to drive their thirst away,
And keeping them from the sheep;
But if they rush dreadful,
The angels, most heedful,
Recieve each mild spirit,
New worlds to inherit.

And there the lion's ruddy eyes
Shall flow with tears of gold,
And pitying the tender cries,
And walking round the fold,
Saying "Wrath, by his meekness,
"And by his health, sickness
"Is driven away
"From our immortal day.

"And now beside thee, bleating lamb,
"I can lie down and sleep;
"Or think on him who bore thy name,
"Graze after thee and weep.
"For, wash'd in life's river,
"My bright mane for ever
"Shall shine like the gold
"As I guard o'er the fold."

Jerusalem's Pillars

INTRODUCTION

TO SONGS OF EXPERIENCE

Hear the voice of the Bard!
Who Present, Past, & Future, sees;
Whose ears have heard
The Holy Word
That walk'd among the ancient trees,

Calling the lapsed Soul,
And weeping in the evening dew;
That might controll
The starry pole,
And fallen, fallen light renew!

"O Earth, O Earth, return!
"Arise from out the dewy grass;
"Night is worn,
"And the morn
"Rises from the slumberous mass.

"Turn away no more;
"Why wilt thou turn away?
"The starry floor,
"The wat'ry shore,
"Is giv'n thee till the break of day."

THE EVERLASTING GOSPEL

TWO EXTRACTS

The Vision of Christ that thou dost see
Is my Vision's Greatest Enemy:
Thine has a great hook nose like thine,
Mine has a snub nose like to mine:
Thine is the friend of All Mankind,
Mine speaks in parables to the Blind:
Thine loves the same world that mine hates,
Thy Heaven doors are my Hell Gates.
Socrates taught what Meletus
Loath'd as a Nation's bitterest Curse,
And Caiphas was in his own Mind
A benefactor to Mankind:
Both read the Bible day & night,
But thou read'st black where I read white . . .

Was Jesus Humble? or did he
Give any Proofs of Humility?
Boast of high Things with Humble tone,
And give with Charity a Stone?
When but a Child he ran away
And left his Parents in dismay.
When they had wander'd three days long
These were the words upon his tongue:
"No Earthly Parents I confess:
"I am doing my Father's business."
When the rich learned Pharisee
Came to consult him secretly,
Upon his heart with Iron pen
He wrote, "Ye must be born again."

A VOICE CAME FORTH

"The morning comes, the night decays, the watchmen
    leave their stations;
"The grave is burst, the spices shed, the linen wrapped
    up;
"The bones of death, the cov'ring clay, the sinews
    shrunk & dry'd
"Reviving shake, inspiring move, breathing, awakening,
"Spring like redeemed captives when their bonds &
    bars are burst.
"Let the slave grinding at the mill run out into the
    field,
"Let him look up into the heavens & laugh in the
    bright air;
"Let the inchained soul, shut up in darkness and in
    sighing,
"Whose face has never seen a smile in thirty weary
    years,
"Rise and look out; his chains are loose, his dungeon
    doors are open;
"And let his wife and children return from the
    oppressor's scourge.

"They look behind at every step & believe it is a dream,
"Singing: 'The Sun has left his blackness & has found
    a fresher morning,
" 'And the fair Moon rejoices in the clear & cloudless
    night;
" ' For Empire is no more, and now the Lion & Wolf
    shall cease.' "

from AMERICA

CREATION

But those in Great Eternity Met in the Council of God
As One Man, hovering over Gilead & Hermon.
He is the Good Shepherd, He is the Lord & Master
To Create Man Morning by Morning, to give gifts at
    Noon day.

Enion brooded o'er the rocks; the rough rocks groaning
    vegetate.
Such power was given to the Solitary wanderer:
The barked Oak, the long limb'd Beech, the Chestnut
    tree, the Pine,
The Pear tree mild, the frowning Walnut, the sharp
    Crab, & Apple sweet,
The rough bark opens; twittering peep forth little beaks
    & wings,
The Nightingale, the Goldfinch, Robin, Lark, Linnet
    & Thrush.
The Goat leap'd from the craggy cliff, the Sheep awoke
    from the mould,
Upon its green stalk rose the Corn, waving innumerable,
Infolding the bright Infants from the desolating winds.

from VALA, OR THE FOUR ZOAS,
Night the First

DESOLATION

"Why does the Raven cry aloud and no eye pities her?
"Why fall the Sparrow & the Robin in the foodless
  winter?
"Faint, shivering, they sit on leafless bush or frozen
  stone

"Wearied with seeking food across the snowy waste,
  the little
"Heart cold, and the little tongue consum'd that once
  in thoughtless joy
"Gave songs of gratitude to waving cornfields round
  their nest.

"Why howl the Lion & the Wolf? why do they roam
  abroad?
"Deluded by summer's heat, they sport in enormous
  love
"And cast their young out to the hungry wilds &
  sandy desarts.

"Why is the Sheep given to the knife? the Lamb plays
  in the Sun:
"He starts! he hears the foot of Man! he says: Take
  thou my wool,
"But spare my life: *but* he knows not that winter
  cometh fast.

"The Spider sits in his labour'd Web, eager watching
  for the Fly.
"Presently comes a famish'd Bird & takes away the
  Spider.
"His Web is left all desolate that his little anxious heart
"So careful wove & spread it out with sighs and
  weariness."

from VALA, OR THE FOUR ZOAS,
Night the First

THE LAMENT OF ENION

"What is the price of Experience? do men buy it for a
   song?
"Or wisdom for a dance in the street? No, it is bought
   with the price
"Of all that a man hath, his wife, his children.
"Wisdom is sold in the desolate market where none
   come to buy,
"And in the wither'd field where the farmer plows for
   bread in vain.

"It is an easy thing to triumph in the summer's sun
"And in the vintage & to sing on the waggon loaded
   with corn.
"It is an easy thing to talk of patience to the afflicted,
"To speak the laws of prudence to the houseless
   wanderer,
"To listen to the hungry raven's cry in wintry season
"When the red blood is fill'd with wine & with the
   marrow of lambs . . .

"Then the groan & the dolor are quite forgotten, &
   the slave grinding at the mill,
"And the captive in chains, & the poor in the prison, &
   the soldier in the field
"When the shatter'd bone hath laid him groaning
   among the happier dead.

"It is an easy thing to rejoice in the tents of prosperity:
"Thus could I sing & thus rejoice: but it is not so with
   me."

from VALA, OR THE FOUR ZOAS,
Night the Second

JERUSALEM

And did those feet in ancient time
Walk upon England's mountains green?
And was the holy Lamb of God
On England's pleasant pastures seen?

And did the Countenance Divine
Shine forth upon our clouded hills?
And was Jerusalem builded here
Among these dark Satanic Mills?

Bring me my Bow of burning gold:
Bring me my Arrows of desire:
Bring me my Spear: O clouds unfold!
Bring me my Chariot of fire.

I will not cease from Mental Fight,
Nor shall my Sword sleep in my hand
Till we have built Jerusalem
In England's green & pleasant Land.

from the Preface to MILTON

ALBION IN DARKNESS

The banks of the Thames are clouded! the ancient porches
    of Albion are
Darken'd! they are drawn thro' unbounded space,
    scatter'd upon
The Void in incoherent despair! Cambridge & Oxford
    & London
Are driven among the starry Wheels, rent away and
    dissipated
In Chasms & Abysses of sorrow, enlarg'd without
    dimension, terrible.
Albion's mountains run with blood, the cries of war &
    of tumult
Resound into the unbounded night, every Human
    perfection
Of mountain & river & city are small & wither'd &
    darken'd . . .

Trembling I sit day and night, my friends are astonish'd
    at me,
Yet they forgive my wanderings. I rest not from my
    great task!
To open the Eternal Worlds, to open the immortal Eyes
Of Man inwards into the Worlds of Thought, into
    Eternity
Ever expanding in the Bosom of God, the Human
    Imagination.

from JERUSALEM, Chapter I

A VISION OF THE NEW JERUSALEM

What are those golden builders doing? where was the
    burying-place
Of soft Ethinthus? near Tyburn's fatal Tree? is that
Mild Zion's hill's most ancient promontory, near mournful
Ever weeping Paddington? is that Calvary and Golgotha
Becoming a building of pity and compassion? Lo!
The stones are pity, and the bricks, well wrought
    affections
Enamel'd with love & kindness, & the tiles engraven gold,
Labour of merciful hands: the beams & rafters are
    forgiveness:
The mortar & cement of the work, tears of honesty:
    the nails
And the screws & iron braces are well wrought
    blandishments
And well contrived words, firm fixing, never forgotten,
Always comforting the remembrance: the floors,
    humility:
The cielings, devotion: the hearths, thanksgiving.
Prepare the furniture, O Lambeth, in thy pitying looms,
The curtains, woven tears & sighs wrought into lovely
    forms
For comfort; there the secret furniture of Jerusalem's
    chamber
Is wrought. Lambeth! the Bride, the Lamb's Wife,
    loveth thee.
Thou art one with her & knowest not of self in thy
    supreme joy.
Go on, builders in hope, tho' Jerusalem wanders far away
Without the gate of Los, among the dark Satanic
    wheels.

from JERUSALEM, Chapter I

85

LONDON

The fields from Islington to Marybone,
To Primrose Hill and Saint John's Wood,
    Were builded over with pillars of gold,
And there Jerusalem's pillars stood.

Her Little-ones ran on the fields,
The Lamb of God among them seen,
    And fair Jerusalem his Bride,
Among the little meadows green.

Pancrass & Kentish-town repose
Among her golden pillars high,
    Among her golden arches which
Shine upon the starry sky.

The Jew's-harp-house & the Green Man,
The Ponds where Boys to bathe delight,
    The fields of Cows by Willan's farm,
Shine in Jerusalem's pleasant sight.

She walks upon our meadows green,
The Lamb of God walks by her side,
    And every English Child is seen
Children of Jesus & his Bride.

from JERUSALEM, To the Jews

ENGLAND! AWAKE!

England! awake! awake! awake!
    Jerusalem thy Sister calls!
Why wilt thou sleep the sleep of death
    And close her from thy ancient walls?

Thy hills & valleys felt her feet
    Gently upon their bosoms move:
Thy gates beheld sweet Zion's ways:
    Then was a time of joy and love.

And now the time returns again:
    Our souls exult, & London's towers
Recieve the Lamb of God to dwell
    In England's green & pleasant bowers.

from JERUSALEM, To the Christians

HEAVEN'S GATE

I give you the end of a golden string,
  Only wind it into a ball,
It will lead you in at Heaven's gate
  Built in Jerusalem's wall.

from JERUSALEM,
To the Christians

INDEX OF FIRST LINES

INDEX OF FIRST LINES